NEUGEBAUER PRESS LONDON, BOSTON

COPYRIGHT © 1982, VERLAG NEUGEBAUER PRESS, SALZBURG, AUSTRIA
ORIGINAL TITLE: PHILIPP GEGEN DEN WÜRFEL
COPYRIGHT © 1982, ENGLISH EDITIONS, NEUGEBAUER PRESS U.S.A.INC., BOSTON
PUBLISHED IN U.S.A. BY NEUGEBAUER PRESS U.S.A.INC.,
DISTRIBUTION BY ALPHABET PRESS, BOSTON.
DISTRIBUTION IN CANADA BY GROLIER LTD., TORONTO.
PUBLISHED IN U.K. BY NEUGEBAUER PRESS PUBLISHING LTD, LONDON.
DISTRIBUTION BY A&C BLACK, LONDON.
PRINTED IN AUSTRIA
ISBN 0 907234 19 4

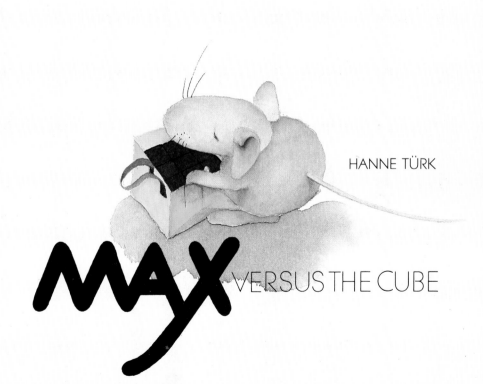

HANNE TÜRK

MAX VERSUS THE CUBE

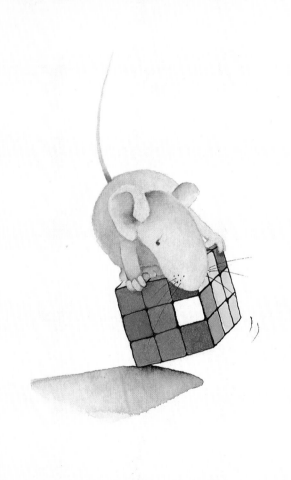

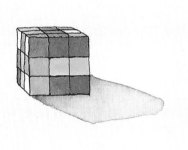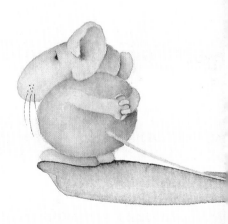